# Psychological 911: DEPRESSION

by

**Michael D. Yapko, Ph.D.**

# A COMPLETE LIST OF BOOKS BY MICHAEL D. YAPKO, Ph.D.

**Hand-Me-Down Blues: How to Stop Depression From Spreading in Families** (1999, St. Martin's Griffin)

**Breaking the Patterns of Depression** (1997, Doubleday/Random House)

**Essentials of Hypnosis** (1995, Brunner/Mazel)

**Suggestions of Abuse: True and False Memories of Childhood Sexual Trauma** (1994, Simon & Schuster)

**Hypnosis and the Treatment of Depressions** (1992, Brunner/Mazel)

**Trancework: An Introduction to the Practice of Clinical Hypnosis** (2nd ed.) (1990, Brunner/Mazel)

**Brief Therapy Approaches to Treating Anxiety and Depression (Ed.)** (1989, Brunner/Mazel)

**When Living Hurts: Directives For Treating Depression** (1988, Brunner/Mazel)

# Psychological 911: Depression

Yapko Publications

Leucadia, CA.

The sole purpose of the **Psychological 911: Depression** book is to be a resource for current and practical information about depression. It is not a substitute for receiving assessment, diagnosis or treatment from a trained mental health professional. Depression can be a very serious and even life-threatening disorder. Consultation with a professional is strongly recommended.

**Psychological 911: Depression**



10 9 8 7 6 5 4 3 2 1

With love, respect and gratitude
to my mom, Gerda Yapko,
who believes in taking the lemons of life
and making lemonade.

# Acknowledgments

My professional life has been quite remarkable. I have had the opportunity to travel extensively in my role as a teacher, and I have had the good fortune to meet and befriend many different people from diverse cultures who have generously shared their views and expertise with me. I thank all of them for making it possible for me to see depression - and life - in a much broader context than might otherwise have been the case.

I have also had the opportunity through my own clinical practice to learn about the pain and despair of depression from very good people who were somehow derailed and just didn't know how to get back on track. I have been moved so many times by their courage and tenacity when they were down, and awed by their grace when they were back up. I offer them all my thanks. People are amazing in their resourcefulness, an observation that keeps me ever intrigued with the professional life I've chosen.

Transcending all is my profound love and appreciation for my wife, Diane. Her honesty, compassion, patience, playfulness, and generosity are inspiring on so many levels. As usual, she had a big hand in this project, and helped make it happen. I'm a lucky fellow to have Diane in my life, and I know it.

My best friends of more than three decades, Wendy, Richard and Megan ("The Hugbug") Horowitz, provide a vital lifeline to sanity more often than they realize. Thanks. You guys are still the best.

Last but not least, my family means everything to me. The Yapko and Harris families continue to provide a loving foundation on which all else is built, for which I am grateful. You're all so easy to love!

MDY

# Introduction

Depression is a complex disorder characterized by superlatives: It is statistically the *most common* of all mood disorders. It is economically the *most costly* in terms of diminished human productivity. It is experientially the *most debilitating*, and is highly correlated with both physical disease and impaired interpersonal relationships. It is potentially the *most lethal* of all disorders, since suicide is so often chosen as the permanent solution to a temporary problem. And, in its favor, depression is among the *most treatable* of disorders we in the mental health profession are asked to treat.

We are coming to a crossroads on mental health issues in the United States. It is long overdue. In fact, on December 13, 1999, Dr. David Satcher, the U.S. Surgeon General and the government's leading spokesperson on matters of public health, released a powerful report documenting the huge gap between the need for mental health services and their availability. He said, "the cruel and unfair stigma attached to mental illness" is "inexcusably outmoded" and must no longer be tolerated. Dr. Satcher wants to pay more attention to mental health issues, and vowed to push this administration and future ones to join his effort.

How do we close the gap between a need for help and its availability? How do we take the massive body of clinical and research data and get it into the hands of the person who suffers and most needs the "candle in the darkness?" This has been my professional struggle all along, and is my reason for writing this ***Psychological 911: Depression*** book. My first five books were for my professional colleagues, and my last three for the general public. I want to bring information to people who desperately need it, and the ***Psychological 911*** series seems a viable way to do so. These are short, easy-to-read books written with the person in mind who is suffering psychological symptoms that impair his or her ability to focus for very long, and who needs quick ideas and clear, current information to help get them back on track in that desperate moment. It's a book for the person who doesn't have the time, energy, or inclination to read books. Its style is "no-nonsense, just answer the darn question."

When I first began studying depression a quarter century ago, very little was known about it. Prozac did not yet exist, the drugs that were available were ones very few people could tolerate (because of their side-effects), effective psychotherapies were not yet developed, and people could only get sparse information at best about even basic questions like, "Who gets depressed and why?" Now, all these years later, depression may well be the most comprehensively studied clinical disorder of all. The body of scientific literature on the subject is enormous. Most important, successful treatments have been developed. The ***Psychological 911*** series can play a significant role in teaching the perspectives and even some of the skills needed to stay sane in an increasingly insane world.

Michael D. Yapko, Ph.D.

# TABLE OF CONTENTS - LIST OF QUESTIONS

## SECTION THREE: PSYCHOTHERAPY

## SECTION FOUR: THE SOCIAL SIDE OF DEPRESSION



## SECTION FIVE: FAMILIES AND DEPRESSION

# What is Depression?

Depression is defined as a mood disorder by the mental health profession. It is a complicated disorder because it can negatively affect so many different aspects of a person's life. For example, it can affect physical health (including sleep patterns, sexual desire, appetite), motivation and attention, relationships with others, job performance, and lead to an overall negative outlook on life. Depression can make life seem joyless and burdensome. Individuals suffering from depression often feel helpless and hopeless about their circumstances ever improving.

Because depression can and does affect many different aspects of a person's life, not all individuals suffering from depression are affected in the same way. People can go to their doctors with quite different symptoms or complaints, yet all may be suffering from depression. Symptoms can also vary from mild to severe. This is why depression may not be accurately diagnosed, even by experienced professionals.

# How Is Depression Diagnosed?

The diagnosis of depression can be a bit tricky because of how often there are other co-existing problems, medical or psychological, that may overshadow or complicate it.

Health professionals use a diagnostic system that is articulated in a comprehensive codebook called the Diagnostic and Statistical Manual, now in its fourth edition, hence called DSM-IV. The DSM-IV lists and describes all disorders, including a number of "Mood Disorders," one of which is called "Major Depression." Major depression, or just "depression," is the most common of the mood disorders and is the subject of this volume. It should not be confused with another "mood disorder" called "Bipolar Disorder," often commonly referred to as "Manic-Depression," which is not addressed here.

According to the DSM-IV, major depression can be diagnosed when an individual has the primary symptoms of:

1) depressed mood most of the day; or,

2) a loss of interest or pleasure in the things you normally enjoy. Depression is diagnosed when either or both of these

persist for at least two weeks. Additional symptoms might include a sleep disturbance (either sleeping too little or too much), an appetite disturbance (either eating too little or too much, resulting in a 5% or more weight change within a month), being noticeably agitated or lethargic, feeling tired most of the time, having feelings of worthlessness, excessive guilt feelings, difficulty concentrating, and thoughts of death or suicide. When most of these symptoms are present most of the time, major depression can be properly diagnosed according to the DSM-IV. What matters more than the "official checklist," however, is how you feel about your own life. If you're suffering, you don't need a checklist to make it "official." If you suspect you may be depressed, it would be wise to present your concerns to a trained professional. (See question on page 78.)

# What Are The Most Common Symptoms of Depression?

While all of the symptoms described in the previous response are common ones, not all are equally so. The most common symptoms of depression are insomnia, fatigue, feelings of hopelessness, helplessness, sadness, anxiety, difficulty concentrating, and thoughts of death and/or suicide. Many people do not experience the other symptoms (such as too much sleep or appetite disturbances) at all, or only very mildly. The symptoms of depression can vary quite a bit from one person to another. The bottom line, though, is how you feel about yourself and the quality of your life.

The symptoms of depression matter because, to a certain extent, they can suggest a course of treatment. For example, the use of medications that can reduce anxiety or enhance sleep while also addressing the depressive symptoms can provide a fuller treatment than if such symptoms are not taken into account. Similarly, a psychotherapy that can teach relaxation and focusing skills in addition to skills in enhancing relationships or problem solving can also provide a more comprehensive treatment than one that overlooks such problems.

# What Causes Depression?

There are many possible causes of depression. Despite widely held beliefs by many that depression has only a single cause (such as trauma or genetics), research has clearly shown that depression is not caused by one single event or a single component of a person's life. Therefore, it is not entirely accurate to promote a one-dimensional view of depression as a purely biological disorder, resulting from a chemical imbalance in the brain, despite its current popularity. Likewise, the one-dimensional view of depression as a product of negative or hurtful events is not completely accurate, either. Depression involves other contributing factors as well. These include individual psychological factors, such as your personal history and your temperament. They also include social factors, such as the culture in which you live and the quality of your relationships with others. Thus, the predominant model of depression in the mental health field is called the "Biopsychosocial" model. It emphasizes the contributions of biology, psychology and social interaction in the development of depression.

# What Medical Conditions Might Be Associated With Depression?

There are many diseases and conditions that can cause or exacerbate depression. Some of the more common ones include: AIDS, anemia, cancer, congestive heart failure, diabetes, infectious hepatitis, malnutrition, multiple sclerosis, rheumatoid arthritis, and thyroid conditions.

The fact that so many medical diseases and physical conditions can be associated with depression is the reason why a thorough physical exam is the best place to begin the process of diagnosis and treatment. While it is true that most depressed individuals do not have a physical basis for the disorder, it remains a wise choice to first rule out any possible medical causes through careful assessment. Treating a physical problem as if it is purely psychological is misdirected effort that can prove costly in more ways than one. Likewise, missing what may be a physical cause of depression means a disease or condition also goes untreated, almost guaranteeing it worsening. Anything that delays effective treatment on all levels contributes to prolonged suffering.

# Can Prescription Drugs Cause Depression?

Yes. There are many prescription drugs that can generate depression as a side effect. Some of the most common ones are those used in treating heart conditions, like beta-blockers, but there are others as well. These include, but are not limited to: Central nervous system depressants, corticosteroids, anticonvulsants, and cancer chemotherapy agents. Individuals taking these drugs and certainly professionals who treat patients taking them need to understand drug effects on mood. Certain prescriptions may need to be changed, or, if they can't be changed for some reason, having a better understanding of the drug's relationship to the mood changes can help individuals better cope with and make decisions about the alternatives available to them.

# Can Drinking Alcohol or Taking Street Drugs Cause or Complicate Depression?

Yes. Alcohol is itself a depressant, and has been shown to aggravate some of the same neural pathways as depression. For someone who is either depressed or is at risk for depression, alcohol is a bad drug and should be avoided completely.

Street ("recreational") drugs also pose a significant risk and should not be used. Their effects on the brain's neurotransmitters are variable and unpredictable. Besides the potential for lasting physical harm, there is also a potential psychological harm that comes from using these substances. They reduce coping skills, and reinforce "escapism" to avoid dealing with one's feelings (e.g., anxiety) or problems. It is disempowering and victimizing to believe that one's problems can't be faced directly or resolved in some sensible way and that drugs will help one cope.

Using alcohol or drugs is a bad decision that inevitably ends up making matters worse. If you or someone you know is abusing drugs or alcohol, it may be a sign of depression and should be addressed in treatment as a top priority.

# What Psychological Conditions Might Be Associated With Depression?

Depression frequently co-exists with other psychological problems. When this occurs, it is called a "co-morbid" condition. Sometimes it matters a great deal which condition dominates the person's experience for treatment to succeed, other times it matters less. In any case, however, it is important to acknowledge co-morbid conditions since they may dramatically influence how to best approach the issues of treatment and recovery.

The most common co-morbid psychological condition with depression is some form of anxiety disorder. An anxiety disorder is a psychological condition in which high levels of anxiety interfere with the person's ability to function well. In fact, many of the most troublesome symptoms of depression may often be attributed to the presence of anxiety: Sleep disturbance, difficulty concentrating, restlessness, agitation and excessive worrying.

Other common co-morbid conditions include alcohol and drug abuse. When someone is abusing some mind-altering substance, whatever underlying depression may be present cannot effectively be addressed until the alcohol or drug abuse is contained. Much of the substance abuse that runs rampant in our society is a product of poorly managed and even unrecognized depression.

There are serious co-morbid psychological conditions known as personality disorders. These are much more complicated difficulties affecting not only what a person does, but who he or she essentially is. Highly dependent people, people with no real sense of themselves, people who avoid facing reality, and people who are very fragile may have problems that are considerably more serious than just depression.

When depression is associated with or seems to underlie other psychological problems, it is especially important not to underestimate one's problems. Effective self-assessment and self-directed treatment (self-help) are not very likely and simply delay getting good diagnosis and treatment, prolonging the misery.

# How Common is Depression?

As of this writing, there are about 20 million Americans suffering depression. About 1 in 4 women and about 1 in 8 men will suffer a major depressive disorder sometime in their lives. The numbers may represent an underestimate, since depression so often goes undiagnosed and untreated.

According to a recent report by the World Health Organization (WHO), depression is ranked worldwide as the fourth most debilitating condition on earth (behind heart disease, cancer and accidents). "Debilitating" refers to a loss of quality of life, human suffering, and the health and social problems known to be associated with depression. Worse yet is the WHO prediction that within the next two decades, by the year 2020, depression will rise from the fourth to the second most debilitating condition on earth.

# What Cures Depression?

Depression experts don't typically talk in terms of "curing" depression. Rather, they tend to speak in terms of "managing" depression. People must learn to manage their moods much as they learn to manage their bodies.

The two main ways depression is managed by health professionals are with psychotherapy and/or the use of antidepressant medications. Both of these management strategies will be discussed in later questions. Self-help strategies are a vital aspect of managing depression.

There are many ways that mental health professionals can help teach depressed individuals to effectively manage their depression. Two essential skills that can be obtained from treatment are learning how to recognize depression's triggers (whether they are in the environment or in your head), and developing ways to prevent the "downslide" with the use of effective life management strategies. Effective strategies for preventing the effects of depression are as unique as the individuals suffering from depression. Collaboration between the individual with depression and a mental health professional is the best means for developing appropriate intervention and self-management strategies.

# Will Depression Ever Just Go Away By Itself?

Sometimes. A phenomenon called "spontaneous remission" can occur in which the depression seems to go away by itself without any deliberate sort of treatment. It isn't known how often this happens, but may occur in as many as half the cases, usually in a range of four to 10 months.

Naturally, people are happy to have their depression eventually lift, and the easiest thing to do is just say "good riddance." However, by doing nothing more active to learn about and deal with the factors contributing to the depressive episode, the likelihood of suffering a relapse is significantly increased. Depression should not be dismissed lightly, even when you're not currently depressed. It requires sustained effort to get over and stay over it, even if "it just seems to go away by itself." Simply put, once you recognize you are vulnerable to depression, it is an ongoing task to manage yourself in ways that insulate you from its effects as much as possible. That requires insight and skill.

# Who Gets Depressed?

Anyone and everyone has the potential to suffer depression. Depression can affect any human being on the planet, depending on the complex interplay between biological vulnerabilities, environmental and social conditions, and personal psychology. The potential to be overwhelmed by life events and/or our own imperfect mental and physical makeup is ever present.

In pointing out that anyone can get depressed, it should be clear to you that depression is not a character defect, a weakness, a shameful condition, a disease, or a curse from God. Depression is a hook in the stream of life that anyone can get snagged on. The measure of mental health isn't about never getting depressed. It's about what you do to overcome it when you are starting to suffer. Clearly, though, some people are more vulnerable to depression than others, an awareness that offers opportunities for prevention.

# Are Some People More Vulnerable to Depression Than Others?

Yes. In terms of age, the single largest group of depression sufferers in the United States is the "baby boomer" generation, i.e., those born since 1945. The fastest growing group is their children (something I wrote about at length in my previous book, *Hand-Me-Down-Blues: How to Stop Depression from Spreading in Families*).

In terms of gender, the largest group of depression sufferers is women. For both social and biological reasons that will be addressed in questions 48-50, women are at risk for depression at a rate nearly double that of men.

Other higher risk groups include:

1) single people, especially if they are unhappily single;

2) people suffering chronic medical and/or debilitating conditions;

3) people trapped in aversive conditions of any sort; and,

4) people who abuse drugs and/or alcohol.

# What are the Risk Factors for Depression?

A "risk factor" is any factor that increases the probability of a particular disease or disorder occurring. For example, smoking is a strong risk factor for lung cancer. In the largest sense, life itself is a risk factor for depression. All people face uncertainty, adversity, loss, and other obstacles to their happiness. But, that is like saying that, "The leading cause of divorce is marriage." Since all people face difficulties in life, why isn't *everyone* depressed?

Biological, psychological and social factors all contribute to the disorder of depression. There are risk factors in each category.

Biologically, although there is no specific gene that causes depression, there is a "genetic predisposition," meaning a genetic vulnerability. A family history of depression suggests, but does not prove, a greater vulnerability to depression when encountering life stressors. Physical illness poses another risk, as described in response to question three. A variety of medications can also trigger depression, particularly heart medications. Your gender is also a risk factor. Merely being a woman increases your risk for depression, for some reasons which are purely biological (e.g., hormonally related to the reproductive cycle).

From a psychological standpoint, the greatest risk factors are associated with your style of thought, especially the way you interpret and react to life experiences. There is a big difference between what actually happens to us in life and the meaning or significance we attach to it. This observation leads to the study of complex psychological issues of personality, temperament, problem-solving skills, values, and many other aspects of psychological functioning.

From a social standpoint, depression often surfaces in the context of human relationships. The deaths of loved ones, the breakups of romances and marriages, the betrayals by trusted friends or authority figures, and other such relationship issues can all increase the risk of depression. When relationships are destructive and painful, depression is far more likely. On a broader level, the culture you live in also poses a risk. Western cultures, like ours, that de-emphasize a sense of community and social belonging tend to have higher rates of depression.

Other general risk factors include: previous episodes of depression, a history of sexual abuse, a history of early losses of parents, alcohol or drug abuse, the presence of other serious psychological or physical problems, and overwhelming stressors. It is important that you remember that a risk factor represents an increased probability, not a certainty.

# Is Depression Ever Normal?

Yes. The fact that human beings come equipped with an emotional life can be a blessing or curse, depending on your point of view. Our range of feelings is impressive, and part of the normal range of emotions are those emotions that can be painful and disruptive. While purging yourself of emotions makes for good Vulcan stories in *Star Trek*, in real life the more sensible goal is to learn how to manage your feelings well, since they are inevitable. Learning to recognize and even to direct your feelings in useful ways is a cornerstone of being mentally healthy.

There are countless situations that can occur in one's life that can trigger feelings of grief, despair, anger, resignation, and other such unpleasant but entirely normal feelings. When someone you love dies or leaves you, when you lose a job that has provided you with status or financial security, when your "reason for being" is gone (such as when your children grow up and leave home), when you face rejection, disappointment, humiliation, and so many other situations that can hurt you, depression can surface.

Here, then, are the key distinctions between "normal" and "abnormal" depression: How bad things get and for how long. When the experience of depression is so powerful that it warps your view of yourself and life in negative ways, when it creeps into your relationships and makes you emotionally distant or volatile, when it infects your quality of life with apathy or pessimism, and it makes life seem a burdensome chore, and these consequences persist in your life for days, which turn into weeks which turn into months, then your depression is no longer normal. "Normal" is when you get hurt, you experience the emotional pain, you endure it without making bad decisions that make matters even worse, and you gradually "bounce back" over a matter of weeks or months. "Normal" is knowing and living the realization that hard times happen, but they don't define the total meaning of life.

# SECTION TWO:

# Biological Considerations and Drug Therapy

# Is Depression Caused By A Chemical Imbalance in The Brain?

The answer is clearly yes and no. To be sure, brain chemistry matters. But people are led to believe a shortage of serotonin or other brain chemicals causes depression, and that simply isn't the whole story. The general public typically hears a lot about the chemical imbalance theory because, first and foremost, drug companies want to sell drugs. Those that suggest an entirely biological view of depression are ignoring the huge amount of irrefutable evidence that depression involves much, much more than just "bad chemistry."

There are many reasons why this information is not as readily available to the general population as are the "chemical imbalance" theories. Advertising money spent by the pharmaceutical companies for depression medications alone was more than $5 billion in 1999. Pharmaceutical companies advertise in magazines, newspapers and television, advising you that if you have "this" symptom, then you should ask your doctor for "that" drug. No other group can possibly compete with such advertising power to put forth other viewpoints.

Another reason that the "chemical imbalance" theory has such strong support is that doctors are trained to define and treat all problems biologically. Also, when you take any of the prescribed drugs, often depressive symptoms abate, at least for awhile, and so the conclusion is that the reason for the depression must have been the chemical imbalance the drug apparently corrected. But, drugs affect people in all sorts of ways. It is not reasonable to assume that if a drug generated an effect that it must have hit the right target.

Last, but not least, there is a cultural shift to explain away all our problems with biology (e.g., "I have a shopping addiction"). It is much more convenient to take a pill than to take personal responsibility for the quality of one's life.

The chief problem with the view of depression as a consequence of a "chemical imbalance in the brain" comes from the recognition that depression can be both caused by and resolved by life events. The misconception is that the brain somehow develops a chemical imbalance and the result is depression, a single directional process. In fact, the relationship between brain chemistry and experience is a circular phenomenon: Life experience affects brain chemistry at least as much as brain chemistry affects life experience. There is a growing body of evidence that psychotherapy, so-called "talk therapy," can alter brain chemistry in ways similar to drugs, without the adverse side-effects.

The "chemical imbalance" hypothesis is not wrong. It's just not entirely correct.

# If The "Chemical Imbalance" Theory Isn't Entirely Correct, Why Is It So Popular?

Only about one in four depression sufferers seek help, and so it is a challenge for mental health professionals to make help more readily available and easier to ask for. So, the strategy was developed to call depression a "disease," one that could be compared to other diseases, like diabetes, that people wouldn't be as likely to blame themselves for or ignore. The strategy has led many to adopt the disease perspective, and its underlying theory that the problem is a problem with the brain. Unfortunately, it isn't the whole picture, or even the majority of the depression picture.

The lion's share of research money in the area of mental health has gone to drug research, far more so than other avenues of exploration. The general public has "bought" the notion that depression is a physical disease that is best treated with drugs. This increases the need for and reliance on medications, even though medications may not be the best approach for a given individual. Patients directly ask for a drug, and even if a prudent doctor were to say, "No, I don't think it's the best treatment option in your particular case," the patient may likely just go ask another doctor. Creating a consumer demand through widespread advertising has been a very successful strategy for the drug manufacturers.

It is tempting to believe the simple act of taking a pill will make the hurt go away. Consider this example, though: A young woman has three young, demanding children. She is married to a man who beats her, and is near impossible to live with. She is unemployed, and financially dependent. In short, her life circumstances are horrible. Is taking an antidepressant medication really the best solution for her situation? Of course not. It is understandable why she would hope that a drug will help her, but it is unrealistic to think that it could. Depression is a more complex problem than simplistically thinking "a pill a day will keep the depression away." Changing her brain chemistry is not going to change her life.

By placing depression in a purely biological framework as the result of a "biochemical imbalance in the brain," the responsibility for depression is directed away from the individual sufferer. It used to be the case, and too many people still believe this, unfortunately, that depression was considered a sign of personal weakness or a character defect. The effect was to blame the sufferer for his or her suffering. Blaming the victim is a poor strategy in any arena, and in relation to depression in particular, it has prevented people who are suffering and needing help from getting the help they need. People didn't want to acknowledge or admit they were depressed, and so they suffered in silence. By calling depression a disease, biology is blamed, and the stigma of depression as a personal weakness can be alleviated.

# Are There Any Medical Tests, Like A Blood Test, You Can Take To Find Out If You're Depressed?

No. There have not been any physical tests developed that have proven themselves to be reliable in diagnosing depression. No blood test, urine analysis, brain scan, chemical test or any other such currently available physical test will accurately reveal the presence of depression. The best and most reliable (though not completely so) means for identifying depression remains a clinical interview with a knowledgeable clinician.

# Is There A Depression Gene That Runs In The Families of Depressed People?

Not exactly. Years ago, before sophisticated analysis of human genes was possible, there existed a belief that specific genes caused specific diseases or disorders. Now, with a far more advanced understanding of genes and their influence on behavior, it is better understood that complex experiences, like depression, are the result of multiple genes functioning collaboratively and in partial response to environmental conditions. This is known as the "gene-environment correlation," and highlights the complex relationship between biological vulnerabilities and the life experiences that can trigger them.

Depression is known to run in families. While genetic predispositions explain part of this phenomenon, family environment helps explain it further. There is no single "depression gene" that depressed people inherit.

# If A Physician Is Told About Some Depressive Symptoms But Doesn't Diagnose Depression, Does That Mean It Isn't Depression?

No. Depression is an underdiagnosed disorder, meaning more people suffer with depression than are identified. Sometimes a physician is presented with symptoms of depression but simply misses the diagnosis. In fact, studies have shown that physicians miss the diagnosis about half the time. The reasons why may be understandable, however. Physicians may have only a few minutes to see a patient, and may not have time to ask the relevant questions. Or, more pressing co-existing physical problems may have priority. Or, a bias towards more readily identifiable physical problems may lead to missing the diagnosis. Or, as is often the case, there isn't time to draw out a patient who is not very communicative.

In any event, since it is only a 50/50 proposition as to whether your doctor will correctly diagnose you, you can't expect your doctor to be a mind reader. You have to be quite direct in presenting your symptoms and concerns. If you can bear in mind that general medical practitioners are not mental health experts, it would be ideal if you would consult a mental health professional for what is statistically more likely to be a reliable and valid diagnosis after your physician has ruled out any medical causes.

# How Do I Know Who To See For Antidepressant Medications?

Under current law, only physicians can prescribe medications. Your physician might recommend you take antidepressants or might recommend you see a psychiatrist. A psychiatrist is a physician (M.D.) with specialized and advanced training in treating emotional disorders. As a physician, psychiatrists can prescribe medications. This is different from a psychologist (commonly holding a Ph.D. or Psy.D. degree) who has his or her advanced training in psychological disorders but is not a physician and therefore cannot prescribe medications. While there are some psychiatrists who offer "talk therapy" as well as medications, many more do not. They will see patients only briefly and for the sole purpose of prescribing drugs, monitoring progress and adjusting drug dosages as may be needed. Psychologists practice "talk therapy" and there are many different kinds which will be addressed later (see question on page 84). There is currently a movement within the psychological profession to obtain the rights to prescribe drugs, too. But until that change is allowed, only physicians can prescribe medications.

If you decide to see a psychiatrist for a medication evaluation, you will be going to a medical specialist. It is best to choose one who specializes in depression. By choosing a psychiatrist with a lot of experience in treating depression, you are more likely to be involved with a professional who has greater training in the appropriate use of antidepressant medication and better ability to follow your progress more closely than general practitioners typically do.

# Do Antidepressant Medications Really Work?

Yes, antidepressants can be helpful to the majority of people who take them as prescribed. Antidepressant medications have been popularly promoted as the "cure" to depression. In fact, antidepressants do not cure depression at all. Rather, they help you manage depression. Antidepressants have the capacity to reduce or even eliminate many symptoms of depression, particularly those known as the "vegetative" symptoms. These are the primarily physical symptoms such as agitation, anxiety, appetite, and sleep disturbances, reduced sex drive, and low physical energy level.

There are advantages and disadvantages to taking antidepressant medications, just as there are in taking any medications. No drug works equally well for everyone who takes it. It is common to try several drugs and dosages before finding the best one for a given individual. No drugs are free of side-effects and potential complications. For example, there is a phenomenon commonly called the "poop-out effect," where the drug helps for a significant period of time, and then simply stops being effective. This happens only occasionally.

In many cases medications can not only be helpful, but life-saving. The decision whether to take medications or not must be made intelligently, not reflexively.

# How Do I Know Which Antidepressant Medication To Take?

You don't. It is not up to you to ask for a specific antidepressant. It is up to the person prescribing the medication to determine which medications and at what dosages are most appropriate for you. He or she determines this on the basis of your symptom profile, medication history, drug sensitivities, interaction effects with other medications you may be taking, age, body size, and other such variables. Some antidepressants may produce secondary effects (anxiety reduction, for example) that are desirable and may be prescribed for that reason.

Even though it may be easier to get a prescription for antidepressants from your general practitioner, internist, or gynecologist, such physicians are usually not well trained in psychoactive medications to either prescribe appropriately or provide good follow-up. Seeing a depression specialist is a very good idea.

Even though it isn't up to you which medications might be prescribed for you, it is up to you to be an informed consumer. You can and should educate yourself about any recommended medication. There are several sources of information including: Asking the physician who is prescribing for literature to read, asking your local pharmacist for information, reading about the drug in books readily available in any bookstore, or getting information on the internet. You should strive to understand what the purpose of taking the medication is, what the risks and benefits are, what side effects may be expected, and how long before results are expected to be seen from taking the medication. Be educated on any contraindications for taking the medication (any previous medical conditions or drugs you might already be taking which conflict with the use of this particular antidepressant medication). Be sure to report any side effects, even mild ones, or other concerns you might have to the prescribing physician. Remember, you are half of the treatment team!

# What Are Some Of The Antidepressant Medications And How Do They Work?

Antidepressant medications are divided into a number of different categories based on their chemical makeup and presumed mechanism of action. The most commonly prescribed antidepressants in the United States today are in the category known as Selective Serotonin Reuptake Inhibitors, or SSRI's. The SSRI's include such drugs as Prozac, Celexa, Paxil and Zoloft. The exact mechanism of action is not fully understood, but is thought to involve a process that increases the concentration of the brain chemical serotonin (called a "neurotransmitter" because it serves as a chemical messenger of sorts between brain cells or neurons). Depletions of serotonin are thought to be linked to depression. The SSRI's are one family of the "new generation" of antidepressants, and have only been in use in America since 1988.

The older generations of antidepressants included the "Tricyclic" antidepressants (named for their three ring chemical structure) and the Monoamine Oxidase inhibitors, or MAOI's. These are still in use today, but much less so. Commonly prescribed tricylics include Elavil, Asendin, and Desyrel. These are drugs whose mechanism of action is assumed to involve increasing the concentration of the neurotransmitters norepinephrine and serotonin in the brain. The commonly prescribed MAOI's include Marplan, Nardil, and Parnate. MAOI's are prescribed much less frequently because their side effects can be somewhat extreme. The MAOI's mechanism of action is also not fully known, but is assumed to increase the concentration of the neurotransmitter norepinephrine and other central nervous system neurotransmitters in the brain.

The SSRI's, and even newer drugs that are simply categorized as "Structurally Unrelated Compounds," such as the drugs Wellbutrin, Serzone and Effexor, have stimulated lots of drug research. New drugs for depression are being developed all the time, and many more will be released in the United States in the near future. Research continues to try to better understand how they work and what the long term risks or benefits might be in using them.

# What Are Some Of The Benefits Associated With Taking Antidepressants?

The key benefits of antidepressants are their overall effect on many of the common symptoms associated with depression. These include: sleep and appetite disturbances, low physical energy, diminished sex drive, and anxiety and agitation. When someone is unable to focus and has so much fatigue he or she feels barely able to move through the day, antidepressants can "raise the floor" so you don't feel so low. When you can't sleep or can't eat because you're so agitated, antidepressants can "lower the ceiling" so you don't feel ready to blow through the roof.

Antidepressants, when they work, tend to work more quickly on symptom remission than so-called "talk therapy." When time is a critical factor to consider, such as if one is suicidal or in danger of making irreversible bad decisions rooted in depression (as divorces often are, for example), antidepressants may be especially important. When the person is too depressed to even participate meaningfully in therapy, medications can help make the person a more active participant and thereby make therapy a more meaningful and helpful endeavor.

Unlike psychotherapy ("talk therapy"), which relies heavily on the skill level of the clinician, drug responses are less dependent on the skill level of the prescriber. How drugs are prescribed matters, of course, but it just isn't as variable as how psychotherapy is conducted.

For most (not all) individuals, the risks associated with the newer antidepressants are relatively minor if they are taken as prescribed. They are generally non-addictive (I say "generally" because for some people there is a possibility of an uncomfortable withdrawal from them). And unlike the older tricyclic antidepressants, they are not likely to be lethal if someone either accidentally or deliberately overdoses.

If there are complications, as there are for some people, they tend to show up quickly. This is an advantage in that you are given a rapid signal to alter dosages or change medications. Likewise, if there are benefits, they generally start to show up relatively soon (usually a few weeks) which makes staying on them a more welcome option.

# What Are Some Of The Risks Associated With Taking Antidepressants?

While most of the risks are minor in a statistical sense, that assurance won't mean much to you if you're among the few who respond poorly. It's best to know ahead of time what problems may arise with the particular medication you are taking so that you can catch and correct them before they become really troublesome.

No one antidepressant is clinically more effective (has a higher treatment success rate) than another. That's true even when comparing newer and older drugs. So, it really comes down to finding out which one may be most helpful to you as an individual.

Only 50-60% of people respond well to the very first drug they try. Your doctor, no matter how gifted, cannot know in advance how your unique body chemistry will interact with the prescribed drug. So, be prepared for some possible "trial and error" rounds, because you might well have to try several different medications before you find one (or some combination of drugs) that is helpful to you.

The chief reason the newer antidepressants are considered a big improvement over the older ones is because, for most people, the side effects are fewer and milder. The most common side effects are nausea, agitation, lethargy, impaired sexual functioning, insomnia, headache and tremor. The potential for more serious side effects exists in a very small percentage of patients. An inability to tolerate the side effects is a primary reason why people go off their medication, and thereby lose any potential benefit it might have offered.

Antidepressants are generally non-addictive, and yet some people can and do develop a tolerance to them. The drug "works" for a while, and then stops working. The person stops taking the drug, and a small percentage of individuals will go through an unpleasant withdrawal (euphemistically called the "discontinuation effects" by doctors).

If you are currently pregnant or are thinking about becoming pregnant, taking antidepressants is generally not a good idea. The potential problems appear to be minimal, as no research has shown a relationship between the use of antidepressants and birth defects. But, given the relatively small body of research in this area, a conservative approach may be best.

As of this writing, antidepressant medications have not been specifically approved for use with children. That hasn't stopped doctors from prescribing them, but you should know that there is very little information available about the effects on children's physical and emotional development when they have been on antidepressants. Similarly, no long-term studies (20 years plus) have been done on anybody on SSRI's since they haven't been around that long (only since 1988).

A key problem with antidepressants from a psychological point of view is that they define the patient's role in treatment as a purely passive one. To suggest that "all you have to do is take your pill on time and the depression will go away" is a disservice to the patient. Even when the symptoms do improve, the underlying social and psychological factors are not addressed through medications alone. Thus, the risk for future episodes remains. The higher rates of relapse associated with medication as an exclusive form of treatment is the weak spot of drug approaches. You can't just be passive and expect to conquer depression. You must be active in learning your risk factors and developing the skills you need to manage them effectively.

# Are Antidepressant Drugs Addictive?

In a strict sense of defining addiction, the answer is no, antidepressants are not considered addictive. The large majority of people who take them and then stop taking them experience no significant withdrawal symptoms. They generally should not be stopped suddenly, however. A gradual, medically supervised reduction is typically recommended by medication experts.

There are some individuals, a small minority, who experience some unpleasant symptoms when discontinuing their usage of antidepressants. These discontinuation symptoms include: headache, nausea, agitation and irritability. While the symptoms can certainly be uncomfortable, they are not usually serious.

Long-term consequences, such as being on SSRI antidepressants for 20 years, have not yet been studied since the newer drugs are not yet 20 years old. The early data for those on such drugs for up to 10 years do not show any serious complications associated with their usage, or an increased potential for addiction.

The more difficult concern at the heart of this question is related to physical and emotional dependence. Physical dependence suggests the body's need for increasingly higher doses to achieve a therapeutic effect. While physical dependency is generally not a common concern, a related concern is when the drug stops working and a new drug must be tried. For reasons no one really knows, a medication can initially work well, and so the person continues using it. Then, it seems to just stop working, and so new medications are tried. It is unclear how often this happens, and little is known about what changes or why.

Finally, regarding the emotional dependence, it is possible to become emotionally reliant on drugs and to come to believe "your mood comes in a bottle." If the drug is prescribed without a good explanation of all the factors that influence depression, or if you are told that all you have to do is "take your pill because your depression is all about brain chemistry," then that information can shape peoples' reactions to drugs and encourage an emotional dependence. Medications can and do help, but as I always tell my clients, "You are much, much more than just your biochemistry."

# Can Antidepressants Change Someone's Personality?

No. Antidepressants can help reduce symptoms of depression, and some can even reduce symptoms of anxiety. Some symptoms can be so severe in their effects on your life that they literally seem to control you. And, when they diminish or even disappear, the effects can sometimes be quite dramatic. You can imagine what it must be like to be able to move more easily through life and not "as if always moving through molasses," as a client of mine aptly described her depression. To get your life back, including your energy, sense of humor, and sociability, can seem like a dramatic personality change, but, in reality, the symptoms are gone and what was underneath them was you. Your personality won't likely change, just your ability to let it come through in your daily life.

# Will I Have To Be On Antidepressants The Rest Of My Life?

Probably not. Most experts have encouraged short-term use, usually somewhere between six and 24 months, to obtain some symptom relief and build a momentum for therapy. Others have advocated for an intermediate term use of up to five years. Only a very few experts have encouraged long-term use, or even life-long usage.

The uncertainties associated with the issue of how long to be on medication are some of the factors that rightly concern people about drug treatment. And yet, doctors who are skilled and well-informed can use your observations and feedback, as well as your history and prognosis, to make intelligent treatment decisions with you.

# What About Natural Antidepressants Like St. John's Wort Or The Dietary Supplement SAM-e?

Both of these substances have been heavily advertised on television, in newspapers, magazines, and on the radio. Neither of these is regulated as a drug by the government, and so there is considerably more room for exaggeration in advertising and promoting them.

First, can these substances really help depression? The answer is a qualified yes, meaning there is mild evidence they can. There is a "but," however. Neither of these has been researched very well under controlled conditions. St. John's Wort has been studied in Europe, particularly Germany, where it is as commonly prescribed as Prozac is in the United States. The studies show promise, but are not conclusive because the dosages varied as did the diagnosis of research subjects in these studies. The National Institute of Health is conducting the first large scale, well-controlled research. Results should be available in late 2001. In the meanwhile, the official position of the National Institute of Mental Health is to say it cannot recommend the use of St. John's Wort at the time of this writing.

SAM-e also requires further research. In the cases of both SAM-e and St. John's Wort, the substances may be helpful for someone suffering mild depression if we are to believe the available limited evidence. They have not been shown to be effective in more severe depressions.

Despite these being "natural" substances (St. John's Wort is an herbal extract and SAM-e is a natural enzyme our bodies make), in artificial and concentrated forms, these are also drugs. Like drugs, they have side-effects, something people sometimes erroneously assume will not be the case. The most common side-effects associated with either or both of them are sensitivity to light, gastrointestinal upset and dizziness. They also take up to 8 weeks to provide a therapeutic effect, considerably longer than standard antidepressants.

As a general principle, if you are only mildly depressed and prefer taking a milder substance to antidepressant medications and you are less concerned about the time factor or the uncertainty as to just how effective these substances are, then taking them may be a reasonable option. You can get them "over the counter" from a variety of retail stores including health food stores, and grocery and drug stores that sell vitamins.

# Are There Other Alternative Treatments That Might Help Depression?

Yes. There are many different treatments, described below, that have been suggested for depression by clinicians who will attest to their effectiveness based on their use with their patients. A clinician's recommendation may not be objective, however. Many alternative treatments have not yet been well researched in order to justify saying they definitely do or do not work.

The following treatments have some support in the research literature, but not yet enough to say they are definitely effective treatments: Acupuncture, Exercise, Hypnosis, Kinesiology/Movement Therapy, Rapid Transcranial Magnetic Stimulation, St. John's Wort and SAM-e.

The following treatments have no support in the research literature: Healing ("Energy channeling"), Rebirthing, Oxygen Therapy, Past-life Regression Therapy, Vitamin Therapy, Aromatherapy and Massage.

Might some of these and other alternative treatments to psychotherapy or medications eventually be found effective? For some of them, quite possibly.

Time will tell, and as always, consumer beware.

# Should One Be Hospitalized For Depression?

It depends on the individual and the situation at the time hospitalization is being considered. Generally speaking, the primary condition under which someone would be hospitalized is when the depression is so severe and damaging to the person's life that it warrants closer monitoring and more intensive care. For example, when someone has suicidal feelings or suicidal intent, or has made a suicide attempt, hospitalization can be a reasonable and often necessary choice. In such cases, hospital settings can be a life-saving place of safety, for it is a genuine tragedy when someone ends his or her life, an irrevocable decision, on the basis of depression, typically a temporary phenomenon.

Other conditions for hospital admission might be:

1) if ongoing life circumstances are so chaotic and overwhelmingly stressful that only by being removed from them even temporarily will someone be able to improve;

2) to use the "closed system" of the hospital unit to stabilize behavior ("get

you back on your feet") and /or to stabilize you on your medications; and,

3) if someone is going to have a procedure called ECT (electro-convulsive therapy), what many still call "shock treatment."

Hospitalization is not without its drawbacks. Hospitals are a medical facility, and so it should come as no surprise that the approach to treatment is primarily medical. Mental health units are run by psychiatrists (medical doctors), and the primary staff are psychiatric nurses. Most hospital units will give a passing nod to psychosocial interventions and include counselors, recreational therapists, and occupational therapists, but these are invariably considered of secondary importance to the medications and controlled hospital environment.

Teaching depressed patients to identify themselves as "sick" with the depression "disease" while passively waiting for the medications to "cure" them isn't necessarily the most useful treatment perspective for most depression sufferers. Sometimes the "time-out" in a hospital can provide great relief and recovery from the overwhelming stresses of life. Sometimes, however, it just makes people feel even more fragile and sensitive to the stresses when they face them in the "real world" again.

The decision of whether to be hospitalized, though not unrealistically extreme, is certainly more involved than is outpatient treatment. Most depression sufferers don't fall into the "severe" category or require an extreme treatment. It is a decision to be made carefully. The final consideration, of course, is cost. Inpatient hospitalization is very expensive, and is nearly unaffordable without adequate health insurance. Not all health insurance policies cover inpatient (or outpatient, for that matter) mental health services, so one would have to check on one's coverage to know what one's options are.

# What Is "Shock Treatment" (ECT) And Does It Work For Depression?

Formerly called "shock treatment," the technical term for the procedure is called "electroconvulsive therapy," or ECT. It involves passing an electrical current through the brain in order to induce a grand-mal seizure. Not long ago, negative public reaction and relatively poor studies about its actual effectiveness led to a sharp decline in its usage. But, in recent years, ECT has again grown in usage by psychiatrists around the U.S., almost exclusively in the most severe cases of depression. More and more studies are attesting to the positive value of ECT in treating severe depressions, especially in those patients that have not responded to any other treatment where the depression is potentially life-threatening to the patient.

When the depression is so severe that the person is in physical danger from the symptoms, or when the person is psychotically depressed (with delusional thinking and even hallucinations), ECT may be prescribed. An individual ECT procedure takes about 20 minutes or so from beginning to end, although the actual passing of the electrical current takes only seconds. The rest of the time is spent administering the anesthesia and muscle relaxants and having them take effect, then arousing the patient when the procedure is over. An anesthesiologist is present and provides the drugs as well as regulates the patient's breathing while he or she is under the anesthetic. The patient's brain waves are also being monitored. Electrical conductors are then placed on the patient's temples and the psychiatrist passes a small current of electricity at either one temple (unilateral) or both temples (bilateral), depending on the doctor's clinical judgment and treatment plan. The patient then experiences a convulsion (i.e., seizure) which lasts several seconds. The drugs prevent most visible reactions. Generally all an observer sees of the convulsion is a "ripple" through the body, a vibration, and a curling of the toes. After a short while, the patient is given medication antidotes, and is aroused to consciousness. Usually the patient is somewhat disoriented, and likely to complain of a headache. ECT is usually done in a series of perhaps 10-15 separate treatments performed over several weeks.

ECT is not without its risks. Physically, because it is done under anesthesia, the same level of risk (small, but not insignifi-

# SECTION THREE:
# Psychotherapy

# How Does Someone Know When He Or She Needs Therapy?

Here are some ways to know when you need professional help:

- If you are depressed and have no idea why or what to do about it;
- If you are suffering symptoms that are directly or indirectly interfering with and diminishing your quality of life;
- If your depression is negatively affecting people you love, especially your spouse and children. If you are getting feedback from others that you need help, and you know it but don't want to face it, you could use some help;
- If your depression has led you to develop thoughts of death or suicide (an especially immediate reason to get help);
- If you have no one close enough to you to confide in and get feedback from who can challenge and divert you from some or all of your depressed thinking and behavior;
- If you have repeated episodes of depression; and,

- If you are depressed, you are having to make major life decisions (such as seeking a divorce, quitting or taking a job, dropping out of school, etc.), and your depression may lead you to make a poor decision you'll end up deeply regretting later. Depression is usually a poor frame of mind to be in when making potentially life-changing decisions.

These are some clear signs telling you when you need help. However, the natural tendency when you're depressed is to want to do nothing, even those simple things that would be helpful. So, even though you may not want to lift a finger to help yourself, you have to find a way to get yourself past that reluctance to actively get help.

Don't wait! Every day depression is allowed to just fester is another day lost to unnecessary suffering. If you know you need help, take action *now*.

# What Should I Do When Feeling Suicidal?

Get immediate help. The danger, of course, is that on the impulse of a despairing moment, you could make an irreversible decision that is tragic in its wastefulness of a valuable human life- yours. In all my years of clinical practice I have never seen somebody who truly wishes to die. I have regularly seen people who just couldn't stand the pain anymore. They just can't see far enough into the future to see that things can change, and they can change. Hopelessness is a viewpoint, not a reality. When depression is severe enough that suicide actually seems like a viable option, you must recognize your perceptions are "off." Get help. Get input. Get an ally to help you see past your pain.

It's hard to believe when you're in the throes of depression that the pain will pass and life can turn around and be better than you imagined. But it can, and you really ought to be here when it does.

# Does Psychotherapy ("Talk Therapy") Really Work?

An emphatic "YES!" Thousands of research studies have shown that several forms of psychotherapy are at least as effective as antidepressant medication, and, in some specific ways, even more effective than antidepressants. Certain types of therapy have been proven to be more effective in treating depression than others (see question on page 84). Psychotherapy, like medication, is also good for reducing symptoms and improving one's outlook. But where therapy really shines is in its ability to teach specific skills that not only reduce depression, but lower the chances for later relapses.

For therapy to work, you have to show up. It may be a struggle for you to do so, but you have everything to gain.

# What Is A "Qualified Psychotherapist?"

A psychotherapist is anyone who provides psychological treatment or counseling, regardless of what specific type of therapy he or she practices or what particular type of degree or license he or she may hold.

Mental health professionals must usually be state licensed to practice their profession. The license is granted only when someone has a valid degree from an accredited university, usually (but not always) followed by supervised structured clinical training. Checking on a potential therapist's licensure and qualifications by calling your state's licensing board to confirm his or her licensure and professional standing before you begin therapy is a very good idea.

A psychiatrist is a physician (M.D., or medical doctor) who has advanced training and specialized interest in treating psychological/emotional disorders. In the United States, the great majority of psychiatrists have been trained to think of mental problems as a product of faulty brain functioning. Since most psychiatrists believe medication is the best answer to helping people, they are not as likely to engage in talk therapies as the other psychotherapists listed below. However, each psychiatrist is an individual and some do practice talk therapy as part of their treatment approach.

A clinical psychologist, usually a Ph.D. or Psy.D. has advanced training and specialized interest in diagnosing and treating psychological and emotional disorders. Their focus is generally on the psychological and social aspects of a disorder, especially relevant in the disorder of depression. While there is currently a movement by some psychologists to obtain drug prescription privileges, which only M.D.'s currently have, most psychologists tend to focus on exploring and clarifying the thoughts, feelings, behaviors, and relationships of the person(s) they're treating by using "talk therapies," i.e., talking with and educating the patient.

A marriage and family therapist has advanced training in the marital and familial aspects of the disorders they treat, while clinical social workers often take a larger cultural and community view of the problems they treat. Either of these types of practitioners will have earned Master's degrees (M.A., or M.S.) and will usually have been trained in doing individual psychotherapy as well.

According to research on clinical effectiveness, it is not the academic degree that someone holds that determines his or her effectiveness. Rather, it is the ability of the individual therapist to provide a good learning environment that is warm, supportive, and, most importantly, goal-oriented.

# How Do I Find A Good Therapist?

You'll need to do some "shopping." You should look for someone who is well-trained academically (minimum of a Master's degree), is positive and empathetic as a person, has extensive clinical experience in treating depressed people, is current with the clinical research, has a good reputation in the community, and who is available for providing treatment to you in a consistent manner.

Do not just go to the Yellow Pages or the local health food restaurant bulletin board. Start with family and friends and ask them if they've seen a therapist they liked and found effective. Ask your family doctor, too (but beware of the "medical brotherhood"that can land you in a psychiatrist/colleague's office and on medication right away in case that isn't what you want). Call the local psychological association (or other local professional associations for marriage and family therapists or social workers) and get the names of people who specialize in depression. Websites for some groups are provided in my response to question number 70, and more are included in Appendix E.

Once you have some names, call them. You will likely have to do some interviewing to get someone you feel comfortable with. It's perfectly alright to speak to someone for a few minutes (not a half hour or more) about your concerns, and to ask him or her the following key questions:

1. What is your training and clinical experience?
2. Do you have specialized training in treating depression? If so, what is it?
3. How do you generally approach problems such as mine?
4. Are you available for regular appointments?
5. What can I reasonably expect of you if I work with you?
6. What are your fees, and how long are the sessions?
7. Can you accept my health insurance (if you have any)?
8. Do you ever involve family members in treatment? If so, when?

By asking such questions and listening carefully to the responses you get, you will get a sense of who the clinician is as a person and how he or she approaches cases such as yours. If you like what you hear, schedule an appointment, and plan to use it as a more careful "shopping" time.

If you don't like the person or develop some confidence he or she can help, then move on and continue looking for someone else to work with. It is tough to shop when you're depressed, I know, but finding the right therapist is crucial. A good therapist can be life-saving in more ways than one.

# What Is The Best Type Of Psychotherapy For Depression?

Clinical research has shown several forms of psychotherapy to be the most effective in helping people overcome depression. They are called cognitive, behavioral, and interpersonal therapies.

Cognitive therapy focuses on the relationship between thoughts (called "cognitions") and mood. Depressed people are prone to thinking negative, hurtful, distressing thoughts that can both cause and maintain depression. Depressed people often make errors in the way they think (such as taking things too personally or jumping to hurtful, negative conclusions without objective evidence) that can be identified and corrected with the help of a good psychotherapist who practices cognitive therapy (sometimes called cognitive therapists).

Behavior therapy focuses on the behaviors associated with depression, especially those that are self-destructive (such as impulsivity, alcohol abuse, or poor time management). The treatment emphasizes learning how to be more effective in the things you do so you can feel better about who you are. These psychotherapists sometimes call themselves behavioral therapists or behaviorists.

Interpersonal therapy focuses on relationships, since so often depression is associated with hurtful relationships. People we love die, friends and lovers desert us, and co-workers, supervisors and kids may sometimes drive us crazy. Interpersonal therapy addresses relationship issues and teaches the skills necessary to keep good relationships healthy, to improve poor relationships, and to adjust well to the changes in relationship when things like death or divorce happen. These psychotherapists may call themselves interpersonal therapists, or marital and family therapists.

A knowledgeable therapist, whatever the degree or license, may practice any or all of these approaches, singly or in combination.

Choose the right therapy according to your problems. If you know or suspect your thinking is "off," then find a psychotherapist with an emphasis or specialty in cognitive therapy. If you behave in ways that add to your distress, see a psychotherapist with an emphasis in behavioral therapy. If your relationships hurt you, then choose a psychotherapist with a specialty in interpersonal therapy.

# Does Someone Have To Go To Therapy For Years In Order To Get Better?

No. When the problem is major depression, and there aren't any other serious co-existing psychological or physical problems to complicate things, therapy is usually a short-term process. In fact, each of the principal therapies for depression (cognitive, behavioral and interpersonal) are time-limited approaches. In other words, they are not therapies that will go on for years as some approaches did in the past. The main reason for the shorter term treatment is because therapists have learned it is not necessary to explore your childhood in depth in order to improve your future. Treatment focuses on identifying what needs to be done and how to get on with doing it.

Most people will have about a dozen sessions. Usually they'll notice improvement after just a few weeks and feel much better after a couple of months. Once the depression has lifted, there will be a few more sessions to strive to prevent any backsliding.

Sometimes, though, someone's problems are more complex than major depression alone. Sometimes the person is drinking heavily, or suffering panic attacks, or is in a violent relationship, or suffers any of a number of other problems that are at least as immediate as the depression. In such cases, therapy may go on longer than a mere dozen sessions in order to get over the mountain of problems. But, the same key principles apply: Therapy is meant to help, and the process should show regular progress towards specific goals.

# What Should One Expect From Therapy?

It's essential that your expectations of therapy be realistic in order to avoid disappointment. You should expect a well-trained clinician to gather relevant information about your symptoms, and the many factors that might have contributed to them. You should expect the clinician to clearly be on your side, a welcome supportive ally in addressing your problems. He or she should be clearly focused on reducing symptoms and addressing associated problems. Therapy should focus on building specific skills, whether it's clear thinking, effective behavior, and/or relationship skills, and should provide a comfortable environment for talking about and learning them. You can expect an informed consent, i.e., a discussion of the therapy approaches to be used and why. You should expect your therapist to give you things to do ("homework assignments") and things to read in-between sessions (and you should do them!). You should expect this person to make use of other resources (such as medication or community support groups) when appropriate. You should expect that everything that is said between you will be held in the strictest confidence.

(Confidentiality can only be broken if you are a danger to yourself or to others, or if you are abusing a child or an elderly person.)

You should not expect the clinician to be your friend or surrogate parent. The relationship may be a close one, but it is still a professional one. And while you should expect the clinician to be on your side, interested in helping you reach your goals, you should not expect him or her to support you in every way or agree with everything you say. Consequently, you should expect to sometimes hear things you'd rather not, or to be pushed to do things that you're a little uncomfortable with, but only when you see the wisdom in learning an important skill outside your "comfort zone." You can expect to be "pushed" a little, but at an acceptable rate. You should expect prompt return phone calls, but you should not expect to have spontaneous sessions over the phone except in the most urgent of circumstances. You should expect to discuss openly any and all factors affecting your work together, including time, money, schedules, expectations, disappointments, and the quality of your relationship.

In short, you should expect professionalism provided in the service of clear therapeutic goals.

# What Happens In A Typical Therapy Session?

Talking, sharing, educating, confronting, supporting, experimenting and growing. Usually the client begins by reporting back to the therapist the things he or she has started to do differently, or what he or she is noticing about his or her symptoms since the previous session. Sometimes, significant events have occurred in-between sessions that the client will report to the therapist, other times the discussion simply picks up where it left off the last time. The discussion typically focuses on specific skills the therapist wants to teach the client, and the offering of guidance as to what the client can do to respond effectively to some issue or problem.

The quality of interaction between a therapist and client can vary quite a bit depending on circumstances and treatment style. Some therapists are more likely to ask about and explore your feelings, while others are more likely to discuss alternatives for resolving problems you're dealing with. Some may hesitate to give you direct advice as to what to do, while others will be very forthright in helping devise a plan and encouraging you to follow it.

Sessions usually range from 45 to 60 minutes in length. In that time, many topics may be considered, or the focus may be on only one. Usually the therapist will also suggest things for you to read or exercises you can do as "homework" that will help you develop the skills he or she thinks will be helpful for you to learn. Research indicates that people who do homework assignments have a better and faster rate of recovery.

# Do People Usually Go To Therapy Alone Or Do They Also Take A Spouse and/or Family?

It's a judgment call. Generally, if your depression relates to something about your family or marriage, it's best to include others in the therapy process. The same is true if your depression is now or has in the past affected them (such as your kids having to take over your responsibilities if you were too down to function, or if your spouse had to cover for you at your job, or if you withdrew from your family and prevented closeness). Even if you recognize that including others in your treatment makes sense, you may still want to have some initial sessions of one-on-one with the therapist to get your issues clear and devise a sensible strategy for addressing them. When you first interview therapists, you can let them know you're thinking of individual sessions initially, but may soon want to bring in other family members (assuming they're willing to participate which, hopefully, they will be). Make sure the therapist knows if you want to include others in your therapy sessions since some clinicians will only work with individuals. Then the two of you can decide together when the best time might be to bring in others.

Sometimes people who finally decide to go for therapy are anxious about it, or are shy or hesitant about it. If someone wants a friend or family member to come to the appointment with them and wait in the waiting room, that's perfectly alright with most clinicians. Whatever it takes to get the recovery process started, most therapists will be willing to do.

# When Therapy Ends, Then What?

When you and your therapist agree that not only has your depression lifted, but the risk factors for backsliding have been well addressed, you may decide to end the therapy. Good! No one should be in therapy any longer than he or she needs to be. Next begins the phase of settling back into a regular life, armed with new knowledge, new awareness, and new strategies for handling life challenges without getting overwhelmed and falling back into old patterns of depression.

But, sometimes life throws us the unexpected, and we do get overwhelmed. Even though your formal therapy may have ended, your relationship with the therapist is now well established. Before things get bad, before you slide into another episode of depression, before you develop serious symptoms, get back in to see the therapist and get some fresh input on how to take a hard time and prevent it from getting much worse. ALWAYS strive to solve problems as quickly as possible, prevent them whenever possible, and use your resources to keep depression at bay. Therapy may end, but going back for additional sessions is not only realistic when times get hard, but it is the intelligent thing to do. It's such a simple way to help keep things from deteriorating.

# SECTION FOUR:
# The Social Side of Depression

# What Are The Social Factors That Can Contribute To Depression?

All people undergo the process of socialization, learning how to think and act as a member of both a family and a larger society. The values you learn, the things you get rewarded or punished for, and the things you learn about life all shape your perception of reality. These things either increase or decrease your vulnerability to depression.

Depression exists in a social context. People are influenced by other people, and we can contribute to each other's depression in subtle ways without even realizing it. The obvious ways people victimize each other in abusive and damaging ways (violence, neglect, exploitation, domination, dehumanization) are bad enough and are generally reliable paths to depression. But the more subtle social influences can be every bit as damaging. Consider the larger cultural influences first which are best represented, I believe, by the media. Consider the effects of our cultural preoccupation with thinness, youth and beauty on generations of women who come to hate themselves for not being 5'8", blond, and weighing 110 pounds, or the men who hate themselves for not being 6'1", lean and muscular. Consider also the effects of a cultural acceptance of easy divorces on a generation of young people being raised to think that scheduled visitation with your mom or dad every other weekend is a normal or acceptable family condition. If you consider the effects of any social movement on the individuals who are most likely to be injured by it, you'll better understand why depression is spreading even more rapidly with each step in the direction of social and family deterioration.

No person is immune to the influence of others, and when the influence of others is negative and people feel victimized, depression is a common consequence. It's important to understand that negative social influences can come from impersonal sources, such as movies and television, as readily as from personal sources, like parents or siblings.

# Is Depression Any Different In Other Cultures, Or Is It Pretty Much The Same Throughout The World?

Depression feels lousy no matter where you happen to live, or what language you happen to speak. But, the rates and quality of depression do differ significantly from culture to culture. In fact, there are some cultures where depression is a relatively minor problem, and other cultures where it is a huge problem. (In the United States, it's a very big problem.) Likewise, the quality of the depressive symptoms differs from culture to culture. In China, for example, the symptoms are more likely to be physical. In the United States, there's a higher probability of guilt feelings reported.

Noticing cultural differences is one of the primary ways we have come to know that viewing depression as if it is only one individual's biological problem is a terribly inadequate perspective of the disorder. Different cultures emphasize different values, viewpoints, relationships, coping strategies, and other such vital aspects of life. These will either increase or decrease the likelihood of depression in a given member of that culture.

It's interesting to note that as societies become westernized (more like the United States), the rates of depression begin to rise. There is clearly something harmful to people's mental health when they become technologically oriented, focused on self-satisfaction and personal gain, removed from the natural cycles of nature, socially isolated, focused on monetary gain and material possessions, and absorbed in other such lifestyle factors.

# What Are Some Of The Cultural Influences In The United States That Seem To Contribute To The Rising Rate Of Depression?

In the United States, and in other western cultures as well, there are many factors that can, singly and in combination, contribute to depression. I'll mention just a few of them. First, we know that people who are involved in healthy, loving, committed relationships suffer less depression. But, such relationships are on the decline. The national divorce rate in the U.S. is over 50%, and, on average, people change jobs every few years and move from one place to another every few years. Thus, having strong, stable connections to family and friends is on the decline, and there is a direct consequence of greater loneliness, unhappiness, and a sense of isolation.

Second, people are being run by technology more than they are running it. Computers, the internet, satellite dishes, and many other attention-absorbing devices consume our time and energy, often with depressing results. For example, there are now studies that conclude that the more you use the internet, the more depressed you are likely to become. The de-emphasis on relationships and real human contact is evident with the more time you spend in front of the computer screen. Television currently occupies most people's spare time; the average American watches somewhere between 30-40 hours per week! People flood their brains with violent images and inane dialogue, and instead of being outside living life, they sit inside and watch other people living scripted lives. And, too often, they come to think that the world of television represents reality or else a quality of life to strive for. Then, when they discover it doesn't really exist, they become disillusioned.

Third, the cultural emphasis on immediate gratification ("Do it now") makes for a population of people with little or no frustration tolerance, a necessary ingredient for effective problem-solving. Most things that are worthwhile take time to create or to learn. Without patience, it's too easy to just skim the surface of life. Overcoming depression doesn't happen overnight, but low frustration tolerance prevents many from even making a realistic effort to strive to overcome it.

Fourth, the cultural emphasis on image over substance ("vote for John Smith, a proud American") leads people to approach complex problems with simple solutions ("Take Prozac") that can only lead to partial success at best. Then, when people fail, they tend to think they're failures, and depression may well set in.

Fifth, there is now a much greater preoccupation with self and self-gratification. The greater the self-absorption, the greater the likelihood of depression. People too easily forget that there are more important things in life than their own comfort or self-indulgence. As far as depression goes, the people who are attached to something greater than themselves do better.

There are many other contributing factors, of course, but these represent some of the most important ones.

# Are Men And Women Equally Depressed?

No. Numerous studies show that women are nearly twice as likely to suffer depression as men. This gender difference leads to a better understanding of some of the factors contributing to depression in all people. Some of the factors are biological, and are associated with the hormonal fluctuations related to reproductive events, such as the onset of menses, menstruation cycles, pregnancy and menopause. These are strong influences, and no man is at risk for suffering a hormonally-based post-partum depression.

But the lives of women are influenced by more than just their biology. There are also social inequities that place women at higher risk as well. Women are more likely to face serious victimizing circumstances such as childhood sexual abuse or domestic violence. Women also routinely face more sexual harassment and sexism (such as lower pay for equivalent work). Women are more likely to be living at the poverty level than men, and are more likely to get hurt financially in unfair divorce settlements. In terms of paths into depression, women are more likely to react to relationship problems, while men tend to react more to threats to their status and self-esteem.

There are those who suggest that the rate of depression between men and women is equal, and men simply express depression differently (usually by "acting out" with violence or substance abuse) and so aren't as likely to be diagnosed. But, without the symptoms of depression, and only inferring them from destructive behavior, how do we know it's truly depression? In any event, it is clear that women's hormonal fluctuations do pose an extra risk that men don't face and help account for the consistently higher rates of depression found in women across numerous studies.

# Do Men And Women Have Differences In Their Way Of Being Depressed Or Reacting To Their Depression?

Yes. While men and women may have some similar and some different pathways into depression, once they're depressed, it is equally distressing. However, there is another gender difference that has taught clinicians a lot about what it takes to recover. It's called "coping style." Women tend to have a more ruminative coping style than men, meaning they are more likely to spin their hurtful and negative thoughts around and around while trying to better understand their own feelings or reactions. "Why is this happening to me?" is an example of a potentially ruminative question. It doesn't suggest any course of corrective action. Men are more likely to have an active coping style, meaning when they encounter problems they generally want to do something about them, even if the course of action chosen is a foolish one that ends up making matters worse. (The goal, of course, is to take sensible, effective action.)

While women may generally be more "emotionally attuned," it's men's action orientation that is often the better response to depression if recovery is the goal. Those therapies that only focus on exploring and expressing your feelings have consistently been shown to be less effective than those that teach active problem-solving skills. In fact, some clinicians have described what they call the "analysis paralysis," the worsening of symptoms when someone does too much analyzing and not enough implementing of goal-oriented strategies.

# At What Age Do Gender Differences Emerge?

Around puberty. Up until puberty, boys and girls have about the same rates of depression, although some research suggests that boys may even suffer slightly more depression than girls. But at puberty, things change. Hormones and moods fluctuate, and social expectations change. Girls who were smart, athletic and confident now get viewed in the light of their sexual desirability. Despite the advances of feminism, socialization pressures still favor getting a boyfriend and later a husband. Girls too often learn that their brains no longer matter as much as their looks. The messages given to girls in our culture aren't very empowering, and it will take a pretty sophisticated and "tuned-in" parent to help his or her daughter learn to counter such devaluing messages.

Boys face their fare share of pressures, too. Some experts suggest that boys' depression is just as rampant as girls', but gets channeled into aggression and other "acting out" behaviors such as drug abuse and alcoholism. Boys are socialized to be emotionally bottled up ("big boys don't cry") and competitive, and might therefore be less likely to report problems with their mood.

The reality is that any group and every group can claim to suffer unfairly in life. After all, everybody suffers some form of bias, and no one gets everything they want. The right to declare oneself a victim, though, does nothing to overcome depression.

# SECTION FIVE:

# Families and Depression

# Does Depression Run In Families?

Yes. There is a 1.5 to 3 times greater likelihood of depression occurring among first-degree relatives (parents, children, siblings). The underlying reasons are both a genetic vulnerability as discussed in Section Two, and the social atmosphere of the family. The evidence suggests that the social factors influencing depression are more powerful than the genetic factors. These factors were presented in my book, *Hand-Me-Down Blues: How to Stop Depression From Spreading in Families.*

# How Does Family Atmosphere Contribute To Someone's Depression?

Through the ongoing and repetitive interactions within the family. Just as an individual has a mood, so does a family. Is the family atmosphere serious or playful? Emotionally close or emotionally distant? Mutually supportive or highly competitive? Tolerant of individual differences or rejecting towards them? Problem-solving oriented or avoidant of problems?

Growing up, you have tens of thousands of interactions with your parents and other significant people. Each interaction holds the potential to teach specific skills or perspectives, or not. If you live with demanding and perfectionistic parents, for example, you may well grow up with the idea that nothing you do is right or nothing you do is good enough. To maintain that harmful belief is damaging to all you may attempt to do, whether in school, the job market, or in relationships which can lead to or maintain depression.

Interactions within the family shape your view of yourself and the world around you. The feedback you get in the form of other peoples' reactions to you lets you know what you are expected to do, how others see you, what you can express, even how you should manage your own body. Your self-image is largely (but not entirely) a product of other's feedback.

Families hold the potential to increase or decrease vulnerability to depression in other ways besides just giving feedback. For example, if parents are not good problem solvers and don't actively teach the skills for managing the problems of life well, how will someone learn effective strategies for living? At least some of the depression we see in so many people today arises when they get overwhelmed by problems they just don't know how to manage. As a final point, the values parents teach, either through word or deed, either provide a solid foundation or one built on sand for making decisions in life. If you learn to value money over service to others, or competition over cooperation, many choices you make throughout life will be affected, for better or worse.

# My Marriage Is Stressful. Can This Trigger Depression?

Yes. Marital distress and depression are clinically linked in a variety of ways. Poor marriages predict an increased vulnerability to depression; people who report having unhappy marriages are at least 10 times more likely to either be or to become depressed. Marital distress not only predicts depression, but can actually cause it. The reasons are many, but the pain of feeling trapped in negative circumstances is at the heart of them. Depression can also make a marriage stressful. It works in both directions.

Of those who seek marital counseling, at least one of the marital partners is depressed in at least 50% of the cases. Of those who seek therapy for depression, their marriages are in a distressed state at least 50% of the time.

The quality of one's marriage is clearly a powerful force in shaping one's view of life. Having the skills to build and maintain a good marriage is the focus of interpersonal (including marital and family) therapy.

## Will Getting A Divorce Help Me Get Over My Depression?

It depends on whether the depression of one or both partners is a basis for the marriage suffering. Divorce often occurs to people as a means to escape their marital distress, and occasionally divorce may be the best thing to do under the circumstances. However, more often than not, if the role of depression in the marriage had been sensibly addressed, divorce would have been unnecessary.

Depression leads people to see things far more negatively than they otherwise would have. Instead of examining their depression and striving to resolve it, many people blame their partner for their depression and their solution is to leave. Then they often discover the hard way that "wherever they go, there they are." Without intervention, they simply transport their depression to a new location or relationship.

Before one considers a divorce or separation and throws themselves into one of the most stressful of all conditions, and the whole family into chaos, it would be wise to evaluate the possible influence of depression on the marriage and family. Depression can be resolved, and there may well be a foundation for the family going on together that transcends the temporary setbacks. Staying together even during tough times is what strong and healthy families do.

To be fair, though, it isn't always possible to hold the family together. The important point here is that before a family breaks up, depression's possible role should be evaluated and taken into account. When depression is out of the way, and you're not seeing things so negatively, things typically get much, much better.

# Is Depression Contagious?

Yes. Not in the viral or bacterial sense, but in the sense that moods are infectious. One person's good mood can brighten up other peoples' moods, and someone's rotten mood can contaminate others' outlooks just as easily. What someone shares with others, how you reveal your feelings, what you say or do that will direct people to notice either the positive or negative can have a significant impact on them. And when someone, such as a parent, is continually complaining or drawing people's attention only to what's bad, wrong, or imperfect, the long-term effect is to train others, especially spouses and children, to do the same. Thus, how someone chooses to interact with others will have a significant impact on their perceptions of him or her, and, in turn, what kind of interactions they have. A depressed person can unwittingly but easily train others to want to avoid him or her, or to attract only other negative, depressed people and thereby reinforce the worst in each other.

# How Should Someone Who Is Depressed Behave Around Others?

You don't have to "just act happy." Nor do you have to walk around and spew poisonous negative thoughts and verbage onto others when you're feeling bad. People often think they must "be genuine," giving themselves license to say whatever they feel in an uncensored way. The "let it all hang out" philosophy isn't a very good one, in this case. You certainly don't want to let temporary down times permanently scar relationships by saying nasty things you'll later regret just because you feel lousy.

It's a necessary skill to master your ability to keep from lashing out at others and to especially protect the people you most care about from your negativity. If you need to talk to them about something they could improve or help with, fine. But "blasting" them is not the way to do that. Your feelings matter, of course, but so do the feelings of others around you. If your depression is seeping into your interactions with others, and you feel you can't control yourself, it is a clear indication you need some immediate help in coping.

# Should People Talk Openly About Their Depression With Friends And Family?

Probably. You should at least consider talking openly about your depression to others who are close to you. If they are truly close to you, they are likely to have noticed that there's something going on with you anyways, and you can help them to understand what it is. You can educate them as you educate yourself as to what depression is, what you're actively doing about it, and what things they can do to help support your efforts to recover. They can't do your recovery work for you, of course, but they can certainly support and even participate in it sensitively. If, however, your family isn't the supportive type and will only label you negatively, you may want to be careful about disclosing too much of what is going on with you.

The counterbalance to the "share everything" philosophy is this: You don't want to defer all family decisions and avoid all family responsibilities because of depression. You don't want to train everyone to see you as "sick" or "fragile" and start to treat you that way. After all, you won't be depressed forever. Be sensitive to extra pressures they may face in coping with your depression, but not so much so that you feel guilty about it. That can't help. Acknowledge the effects of your depression on others and you will be likely to get more support than anger.

Having a therapist is helpful for some of these very reasons. Someone well trained who can speed your recovery along, and who can share your burden so you burden others less can make a huge difference. Someone to whom you can vent your negative feelings instead of "dumping" on everyone else can save you from seriously damaging important relationships. Someone who can bring your family together in session to talk about sensitive issues together in a safe, controlled way is potentially invaluable.

Depression needs to be addressed directly. Talk about, but make sure you also *do* something about it. Talking about it just isn't enough.

# Is It Possible To Prevent One's Children From Becoming Depressed?

To a considerable extent, yes. In my previous book, *Hand-Me-Down Blues: How to Stop Depression From Spreading in Families* (St. Martin's Griffin, 1999), I described the family atmospheres and family interactions that can increase or decrease vulnerabilities to depression. This particular question is one of the most important of all, and draws attention to the fact that depression can be prevented to a significant extent in both children and adults.

There are specific skills to master if one is to prevent depression. An effective parent has to be a model of good problem-solving behavior, especially by dealing with problems quickly, sensitively, and with an emphasis on forethought (anticipating the consequences of one's actions). To model passivity, giving up, blind lashing out at others, or a withdrawal from life, sets a poor example of how to deal with personal problems. Modeling a deliberateness about what you say and do, a protectiveness towards others even when feeling terrible, and skill in coping, increases the chances that your children will learn effective strategies for living life. Furthermore, the more time you spend with your children and draw them out about their feelings and perceptions, the more you can teach them how to think clearly about themselves and their lives. The single best prevention is clear thinking, the kind that would lead children to understand, for example, they are not responsible for mom or dad's depression and that they are not fated to duplicate their parents. Other important preventive skills are impulse control, and the ability to do frequent reality checks ("How do I know if this is true?"). Children (and adults, too) need to know that just because they think or feel something doesn't make it so.

# How Should One Handle A Depressed Family Member?

Compassionately, lovingly, and firmly. The last thing anyone needs is to be blamed for his or her depression. People don't choose to be depressed, nor do they stay depressed because it's rewarding. It is the nature of depressed people to be passive and to do little to help themselves. That false sense of helplessness often frustrates and even enrages family and friends, who wish the depressed person could "snap out of it" and "get on with life." But, such feedback is equivalent to telling a depressed person to "cheer up" and "look at the bright side of things." It's meant to be helpful, but such advice typically just makes matters worse.

Here are some "do's" and "don'ts." Don't criticize what he or she is doing wrong. *Do* talk about what can be done differently or better. Don't blame him or her for being depressed. *Do* talk about developing a course of corrective action. Don't assume you have either something or nothing to do with the problem. *Do* check if there is something you're contributing to the problem in some way. Don't curtail discussions of depressed feelings. *Do* know your limits in helping to share the burden. Don't baby the person and treat him or her as "sick." *Do* encourage him or her to do those things for him or herself that can be done independently. Don't dissuade the person from getting help. *Do* assist with finding a good therapist and even with participating in the treatment, if desirable. Don't condescend. *Do* be tolerant. Don't probe too much. *Do* probe enough. Don't ignore symptoms. *Do* discuss them and present them clearly to a clinician. Don't give up. *Do* persist and try different approaches. Don't let him or her stop going places and doing things. *Do* keep him or her active in living life. Don't let someone else's depression become your life focus. *Do* maintain your own quality of life.

It's hard on you when someone you love is depressed. You want to rescue and protect him or her. But, all you can really do is love and support the person, and keep an eye on life together after depression.

# How Does One Get A Depressed Family Member To Seek Professional Help?

There is no easy answer to this difficult question. Even as a well-trained clinical psychologist, my clients can defeat my best efforts simply by doing nothing.

Only about one in four depressed people ever seek professional help. For some it's the stigma ("I'm not crazy!"), for some it's fear ("What if I get stuck in a hospital or get put on medication that changes me?"), but for most people it's just the depression itself ("Why should I bother? No one can help me"). Hopelessness which generates apathy is the most common mindset of depression sufferers. They tell themselves that nothing can help and then make the costly mistake of believing themselves.

Timing is everything. How much will someone suffer before wanting help? Some people head to the doctor right away on a first painful twinge, while others have to be near death before they'll see a doctor. So, the first thing to consider saying to your family member is some variation of this: "I'm deeply concerned about you. You're clearly depressed, and you're obviously suffering. I don't know what to do to help you and I think if you knew what to do to help yourself you'd be doing it. Before things get worse and our lives together get damaged, can we get the help of someone who really understands what to do here?" The essence of the message is, "since we don't know what to do, rather than suffering needlessly, let's find someone who does." The key is not to imply "you're sick" or "you're all screwed up," but to say "we need help in dealing with this. I'm with you."

How far are you willing to go to get your family member some help? And at what point do you intervene? Do you call a friend to try and have him or her be the one to suggest help? Maybe. Do you get the whole family together to collectively say, "You need help?" Maybe. Do you call your family doctor and ask him or her to call your family member in for a visit? Maybe. Is there anyone else in a position of influence with him or her that might help? Perhaps. The importance of overcoming the helplessness and initiating an active approach to self-care cannot be overstated. So, keep trying until you, hopefully, find a way. Bear in mind, though, you can't force someone into voluntary treatment.

# How Do I Know If My Child Is Depressed, Or "Just Going Through A Phase?"

Children and adolescents represent the fastest growing group of depression sufferers. It wasn't very long ago that mental health professionals ignored children's depression altogether, thinking them too young and emotionally undeveloped to experience "true" depression. How terribly wrong. Children do get depressed, and when they do, the symptoms parallel those of adults: Sadness, apathy, hopeless and helpless feelings, social withdrawal, irritability, and behavioral "acting out" (such as aggression). A child who typically was considered happy and easy going becomes less outgoing and rarely smiles anymore. The things that he or she used to enjoy and take pleasure in no longer generate smiles or enthusiasm. The child who used to have friends come over to play no longer socializes, or comes home saying, "No one likes me." The child who has more and more angry outbursts, who sulks and complains "life isn't fair," or starts to behave in any extreme way deserves a much closer look.

Children are dependent on adults, and so are more vulnerable to adult influences over which they have little or no control. Remember the earlier point that anything that has the potential to victimize someone has the potential to depress him or her. So, if a child is exposed to a parent with his or her own impairing depression, or to a nasty divorce, the potential for the child to feel hurt by uncontrollable situations is significant. Yet if you ask the child, "What's wrong?" the most likely response is "Nothing." Be careful not to underestimate the problem, though.

The most important point to consider is this one: When depression has its onset in childhood, the odds increase dramatically that the child will have more repeat episodes later, and possibly each one a little worse than the one before. Thus, the best and most conservative advice is to have your child assessed by knowledgeable professionals. If you wait, thinking he or she will just outgrow it, you may be rewarded by seeing a return to "normal" in some weeks or months. But left untreated, in adults or children, even when the depression goes away, the greater likelihood for later relapses exists.

When a child develops the skills described earlier, namely the cognitive and relational skills necessary to think

# Does Divorce Increase A Child's Vulnerability To Depression?

Yes. Despite parents idealistic wish that they could divorce without hurting their children, the long-term evidence is substantial that divorce increases risks for depression and other problems. Children need two loving and functional parents around as much as possible, and there is a price to be paid when they don't have them. It is not a coincidence that the largest group of depression sufferers, who place great emphasis on personal convenience which includes dumping families when they are no longer convenient, is now raising the fastest growing group of depression sufferers.

Younger children of divorce have an elevated risk for academic problems, engaging in disruptive behavior, and having higher rates of peer conflict. The effect on adolescence is even more pronounced, placing them at higher risk levels for feeling dissatisfied with life, dropping out of school, being unemployed, being sexually active at a younger age, and having a child out of wedlock. Teen moms in particular are highly vulnerable to depression, overwhelmed with parental responsibilities they do not have the maturity to handle while having normal social development interrupted.

The more distressed the marriage prior to deciding to divorce, the more hostile the divorce, the greater the preoccupation of each parent with managing his or her own mood difficulties during such a painful transition, the greater the risk for children of divorce. Parents on the brink of separation or divorce should know to never use their children as weapons, to keep the children out of the middle of the conflicts, and to make sure the children have a support system in place to help them handle their feelings and needs during and after stressful times. Helpful as these tips may be, though, the ideal is to preserve the integrity of the family whenever possible.

# What Should Parents Do When They Disagree Over Whether A Child Needs Help?

The tendency for one parent to overestimate a problem or the other parent to underestimate the problem is inevitable. After all, you have two differing sets of perceptions, and these will surface repeatedly in any interaction where a joint decision must be made. Where a child is concerned, however, it is often the case that one or both parents tend to underestimate the severity of the problem because it is too emotionally burdensome to have to consider that one's child may have a serious problem and need professional help. Many therapists call this "denial," the perceptual twist one makes that minimizes a problem so it won't have to be faced. Before one or both parents fall into a pattern of "denial," they would do well to ask themselves, "How do we know whether this problem we're seeing is serious or not?" When they can't answer objectively and just "feel" it's not a problem, the mandate is to get an objective opinion from a knowledgeable source.

The wisdom in this situation is in knowing that either one or both parents may be "off" in their perceptions. At stake, however, is the well-being of the child. It's true you don't want to rush off to the doctor every time your child sniffles, but it's also true you don't want to downplay a problem that will likely get worse if minimized or ignored. Nor do you want to risk a child's well-being simply because it's inconvenient to see a therapist. You don't have to fear being blamed, nor do you have to be concerned about some stigma, or negative judgments from others. Keep the focus on the child getting better.

Having two parents united in their thinking about what to do next is ideal, but may not happen. At the very least, sitting down with your child (however old he or she is after around the age of 4) and talking about what you've noticed that concerns you and how he or she is doing and how he or she is addressing the problems will, hopefully, give you some sense as to whether a hard time is temporary or likely to be enduring. If it's likely to be enduring because it involves common situations in life (such as difficulty handling mean kids at school or coping with the stresses of having to learn new skills), then getting help is indicated. Your spouse may not want to participate, which is a shame, but he or she can at least get out of the way of your efforts to get help for your child. That's especially true when the parents live apart and the well-being of the child is made more important than winning the parental "tug of war."

# Are Antidepressant Drugs Safe For Children?

As of this writing, none of the most commonly used antidepressants (like Prozac or Zoloft) have specifically been approved yet for children. However, that has not stopped doctors from writing ever-increasing numbers of antidepressant prescriptions for children. There is no good evidence to date that these drugs are effective or safe for children, though studies are ongoing as you read this. Likewise, there is no good evidence that these drugs aren't safe or effective for children. However, there is a lot of anecdotal evidence, in the direct experience of pediatricians, psychiatrists, psychotherapists, and parents, who think the medications have helped children and adolescents.

What are the consequences of chemically altering young, developing brains? No one knows. All the children already placed on antidepressants despite their lack of specific approval for such use will end up being the "living laboratory" and time will tell. In practical terms, however, the effects of depression can have on a developing brain are also detrimental, and so it may seem a difficult choice to make. That's true, though, only if one thinks in extreme "either drugs or depression" terms. Psychotherapy is a non-drug alternative, but is often more difficult to facilitate in children for a variety of reasons. These range from less insurance coverage, or the difficulties of two busy working parents trying to make and keep regular appointments, to the less verbal and communicative nature of children.

# From What Age Might Psychotherapy Be Helpful To A Child?

The age from which benefit can be derived is quite young, perhaps as young as three or four, for even when a child is not yet particularly verbal, non-verbal or less verbal techniques (such as play therapy, role playing, and art and music therapies) can be effective. In even younger children, therapy may also be beneficial by providing parents with new child-management strategies. Child and adolescent therapists are specialists in working with children, and can be quite skilled in getting children to open up and to learn important life skills. Interviewing therapists to find one you like and trust is essential.

For older children and adolescents, treatment models parallel those of adults. Children are taught good coping, problem-solving, and interpersonal skills. These have been shown to not only reduce depression, but also to reduce the likelihood of relapse. And, for those parents concerned about having their child medicated with antidepressants, therapy can provide the benefits without the potential drug side-effects.

# What Should One Do When An Adolescent Refuses To Get Help?

Pushing a child or anyone, for that matter, to get help when he or she doesn't want it is a very difficult situation, and there is no easy answer. The person can defeat your best efforts simply by doing nothing.

The conversation about getting help must be as free of anger or conflict as possible. Instead of mandating "I want you to see a shrink!" which invites rebellion, a better approach may be one that's more empathetic: "I see you hurting and I want to help. I don't know what to do though. Can't we talk to someone who does? I just don't want you to continue to hurt." Choose a time when your interactions are friendlier rather than mid-argument. Go out of your way to create times when talking is possible, such as in the car, or when you are doing some activity together where the focus isn't each other. It's often easier to get an adolescent to open up when the focus is on a shared task. Having had decent communication all along is important, of course. To expect a child to open up when you haven't talked intimately in months or years may be unrealistic. Another option is to find significant others in the child's life like a teacher, school counselor, or even a friend's parent that can step in and encourage some open discussion of problems. Bear in mind that even an angry, sulking adolescent doesn't want their negative feelings to persist. You can impart the desire for things to improve, support their feelings and needs, and offer the wisdom that "doing more of the same makes no sense."

As a concerned parent, you can and perhaps even should participate in the treatment. Allow variations, though. Your adolescent may prefer to start with you present, and then have you leave so he or she can have the "alone time" with the therapist. Or, your adolescent may not want you involved in the therapy at all.

No child or adolescent wants to feel "different" or "crazy." Much of the resistance to getting help comes from that misperception. If you stay focused on what's going wrong that is correctable, though, and you make it easy for your child to get help without having to explain everything to you, you may get a better response to your suggestions for getting help.

# What Immediate Things Can Be Done To Decrease The Chances Of A Child Getting Depressed?

There are quite a few things one can do. First and foremost, strive to get and stay connected to your child. Closeness doesn't just happen, but distance does. It's unlikely, though not impossible, that you can be distant for years and then all of a sudden get close. Talk to your kids constantly. Problem solve with them. Share problems and discuss solutions. Talk about meaningful things, but remember to have fun, too. There is no substitute for good quality time together as much as possible.

Second, turn off the television. The average child watches over four hours per day, and it literally prevents them from getting realistic perceptions about themselves, others, and life. It encourages distorted thinking, and curtails meaningful interaction. TV is an inadequate but convenient babysitter for parents who don't or can't spend time with their children. It's a poor substitute.

Third, limit computer time. Watch what websites your child visits and supervise their time on the computer. The data are clear showing the correlation between the amount of screen time and depression.

Fourth, hold your children accountable for their actions. Be consistent in the consequences, especially rewards, for "right" behavior.

Fifth, beware of yourself as a model. Get used to asking yourself what the message to your kids is as they watch you living your life. As writer James Baldwin said, "Children may not always have listened to their parents, but they have never failed to imitate them." Model social responsibility, timely problem-solving, rational thinking, and the value of close family relationships.

Sixth, teach forward thinking, i.e., how to anticipate likely consequences of one's behavior. So much misery could be prevented with foresight, yet people make decisions blindly on the basis of their feelings of the moment, only to suffer greatly later. Teaching the value of goals and goal-oriented behavior is at least as important as teaching how to enjoy the moment.

# Now That I've Read This Book, What Do I Do Next?

This short book is intended to provide some information and perspective about depression. Hopefully it has provided you with some of the information you will need to begin to sensibly address the complex disorder of depression. With this brief introduction to some of the clinical theory, research, and practice around the subject of depression, you are now better equipped to decide what to do next.

You may have discovered that the most important message written here is that someone who is suffering with depression can do some intelligent things to help him or herself and thereby recover. More information is available to you in a variety of places ranging from websites to books (see the next two questions). Well-trained mental health professionals are available to offer guidance and support in your efforts to overcome depression.

The most important thing now is to keep active in addressing the problems and issues in your life, never giving in to the distorted perception that everyone else can get better, but you can't. Of course, you can. But not by doing the same old things and waiting for a miracle to happen.

The first principle of change is, "Do something different." If you don't know what to do, don't assume nothing can be done. Don't mistake uncertainty for inevitability. Depression is not inevitable. Keep your eye on the goal, and do what it takes to reach it. The future is wide open.

# What Top 5 Self-Help Books for Depression Would You Recommend?

**Breaking the Patterns of Depression**
by Michael Yapko

**Feeling Good**
by David Burns

**Mind Over Mood**
by Dennis Greenberger
and Christine Padesky

**Hand-Me-Down Blues: How to Stop Depression From Spreading in Families**
by Michael Yapko

**Learned Optimism**
by Martin Seligman

# What Top 5 Websites Would You Recommend For More Depression Information?

www.managing-depression-intelligently.com

www.AllAboutDepression.com

www.nimh.nih.gov

www.psycom.net/depression.central.html

www.med.upenn.edu/psycct

# Final Thoughts

# Final Thoughts

It is sad how easy it is to predict that depression will continue to be a growing problem. It doesn't have to be that way, though. We know so much about what it takes to treat and even prevent depression.

But, it is a human failing to not pay serious attention to a problem until it is in the "critical danger" zone. That is not a failing you have to have, though. This short book provides some key information about depression, and equips you with many of the facts and perspectives you need to start to deal with and resolve depression.

The most powerful tool is knowledge. I hope you will use what you have learned here to get the help you need for yourself or those you love who may be suffering. Don't wait. Time is much too valuable a commodity to waste.

# Appendix A

**Focusing on Feeling Good: A Self-Help Audiotape Program for Managing Depression**

I have created a series of self-help audiotapes for depression which involve the use of hypnotic methods of relaxing and focusing. They can teach you to create feelings of comfort while you build a positive frame of mind in order to deal effectively with common problems associated with depression. These tapes can help you to think more clearly and take appropriate action, and thereby better accomplish specific goals and resolve bothersome issues. The tapes are listed below; each is titled according to the specific issue or symptom it addresses.

**FOCUSING ON FEELING GOOD**

Depression as the Problem; Hypnosis as a Solution
(A discussion about how to overcome depression)

The Power of Vision
(Build positive expectations)

Try Again...But Do Something Different
(Manage life circumstances flexibly)

Is It In Your Control?
(Learning to control the controllable)

You're the Border Patrol
(Build self-defining boundaries)

Presumed Innocent But Feeling Guilty
(Resolve issues of guilt)

Good Night...And Sleep Well
(Curtail rumination and facilitate improved sleep)

Prevention Whenever Possible
(Integrate preventive learnings)

Ordering Information for **Focusing on Feeling Good**

**By MAIL:**
Yapko Publications
P.O. Box 234268
Leucadia, CA. 92023-4268

**By FAX:**
858-259-6271

**ON-LINE:**
www.yapko.com

**Formats:**
4 Audiotapes
$39.95 (+ $5.95 shipping and handling within the U.S.)

4 Compact Discs
$49.95 (+ $5.95 shipping and handling within the U.S.)

Be sure to specify the format you want (audio or CD), print your mailing address and telephone number, and provide a check (payable to "Dr. Yapko") or credit card number (VISA or Mastercard only; include the expiration date, your name as it appears on the card and your charge card billing address.)

Please allow 2 weeks for delivery.

Note: International shipping and handling costs vary and will be charged as costs dictate.

# Appendix B

**BREAKING PATTERNS OF DEPRESSION: The Workshop**
A Dynamic, Live Presentation with Dr. Michael Yapko

In this fact-filled, fun and fast-paced five hour workshop, Dr. Yapko shares a great deal of information and, more important, a great deal of insight about the complex nature of depression. He highlights key issues and answers fundamental questions about this serious topic. You now have the opportunity to "sit in on a workshop" when you obtain this enjoyable and informative presentation in any of a variety of formats: Videotape, Compact Disc (CD), or on audiotape.

You can use the material to review key concepts you want to master, or share relevant data with family, colleagues and friends, or perhaps as a means for facilitating meaningful discussion, or in any way that allows Dr. Yapko's work to make an ongoing contribution to your life or the lives of those you care about.

In this professionally recorded workshop program, Dr. Yapko clearly answers key questions about depression, and elaborates on many of the most important issues people face in learning to manage it. The full day workshop is divided into four sections:

Section 1: *The Features of Depression.* Topics include how depression is diagnosed, what we learn from studying who gets depressed and who doesn't in the United States and around the world, and how to think multidimensionally about depression.

Section 2: *Styles of Managing Depression.* Topics include gender differences in depression, how your life perspective can put you at risk, and why there is no substitute for taking sensible action.

Section 3: *Depression in the Family.*Topics include why depression is a family problem at least as much as an individual problem, how depression affects the family life cycle in dating, marrying, parenting and even divorcing, and the potential negative effects of depressed parents on their children.

Section 4: *Treatment Issues.* Topics include the risks and benefits of medications and psychotherapy, choosing help intelligently, and how to think preventively.

• • • • •

Ordering Information for **Breaking Patterns of Depression: The Workshop**

**By MAIL:**
Yapko Publications
P.O. Box 234268
Leucadia, CA. 92023-4268

**By FAX:**
858-259-6271

**ON-LINE:**
www.yapko.com

Be sure to specify the format you want (video, audio or CD), print your mailing address and telephone number, and provide a check (payable to "Dr. Yapko") or credit card number (VISA or Mastercard only; include the expiration date, your name as it appears on the credit card and your charge card billing address) for the full price and add $6.00 for shipping and handling within the U.S.

**Formats:**

Audiotape Program:
(set includes: 4 - 90 minute tapes) ............................ $40.00

Compact Disc (CD)
(set includes 7 compact discs) ............................... $50.00

Videotape (VHS only)
(set includes 3 VHS videotapes) .............................. $60.00

Please allow 2 weeks for delivery.

Note: International shipping and handling costs vary and will be charged as costs dictate.

# Appendix C

Contact Information for Dr. Michael Yapko

**By Mail:**
Dr. Michael Yapko
P.O. Box 234268
Leucadia, California 92023-4268

**By Fax:**
858-259-6271

**By E-Mail:**
MichaelYapko@Yapko.com

**Website:**
www.yapko.com

Dr. Yapko's website includes his national and international teaching schedule, ordering information for all his books and tapes, current events, and links to other helpful websites.

**Bulk Orders:**

**Psychological 911** can be purchased in quantities of 12 or more at a bulk rate discount. Contact Dr. Yapko via e-mail at the above address to indicate your interest in bulk purchasing.

# Appendix D

Organizational Support Information

**American Association for Marriage and Family Therapy**
1133 15th Street N.W., Suite 300
Washington, DC 20005-2710
202-452-0109

**American Psychiatric Associaton**
1400 K. Street, N.W.
Washington, DC 20005
202-682-6220

**American Psychological Association**
750 First Street, N.E.
Washington, DC 20002
202-336-5800

**Depression Awareness,**
**Recognition and Treatment (D/ART)**
National Institute of Mental Health
5600 Fishers Lane, Room 10-85, Department GL
Rockville, MD 20857
800-421-4211

**National Associaton of Social Workers**
750 First Street, N.E.
Washington, DC 20002
800-638-8799

**National Mental Health Association**
1021 Prince Street
Alexandria, VA 22314
800-969-6642

# Appendix E

## Information on the Internet

Disclaimer: The following websites provide information on depression and related mood disorders. They are listed in alphabetical order and are included here as additional sources of information. They are not necessarily endorsed for their content by the author.

**All About Depression**
www.AllAboutDepression.com

**American Academy of Child and Adolescent Psychiatry**
www.aacap.org/

**American Association for Marriage and Family Therapy**
www.aamft.org

**American Association of Suicidology**
www.suicidology.org

**American Psychiatric Association**
www.psych.org/

**American Psychological Association Consumer Help Center**
www.apa.org

**Anxiety Disorders Association of America**
www.adaa.org

**Behavior Online**
www.behavior.net

**Center for Cognitive Therapy**
www.med.upenn.edu/psycct

**Depression and Related Affective Disorders Association**
www.med.jhu.edu/drada

**Depression Screening**
www.depression-screening.org

**Internet Depression Resource List**
www. execpc.com/~corbeau/

**Managing Depression Intelligently**
www.managing-depression-intelligently.com

**Moodswing**
www.moodswing.org

**National Alliance for the Mentally Ill**
www.nami.org

**National Depressive and Manic Depressive Association**
www.ndmda.org

**National Foundation for Depressive Illness**
www.depression.org

**National Institute of Mental Health**
www.nimh.nih.gov/

**National Mental Health Association**
www.nmha.org

**Psych Central**
www.grohol.com

**Self-Help for Depression**
www.self-help-for-depression.com